D1451953

THIS BOOK BELONGS TO:

My Magical Gifts

The Magic of Me Series

ISBN: 978-1-951597-05-4 (hardcover)
ISBN: 978-1-951597-06-1 (ebook)

Library of Congress Control Number: 2020902295

Illustrations by Zuzana Svobodová
Book design by Zuzana Svobodová, Maškrtáreň
Editing by Laura Boffa

First printing edition 2020.

Boundless Movement

Visit www.authorbcummings.com

The Magic of Me

MY MAGICAL GIFTS

WRITTEN BY

BECKY CUMMINGS

ILLUSTRATED BY

ZUZANA SVOBODOVÁ

Tips for Reading with Children

Talk to your child about what gifts he or she received that day. Maybe someone said something kind or did something special. Sometimes these small things will go unnoticed unless we take time to reflect on our day. Bring these moments to awareness by talking to your child about being grateful for them.

After you read the book, discuss one way your child can be giving the following day. Ask your child to pick a person to honor with a gift. Brainstorm ideas of what he or she might say or do. You can suggest ideas from the book or see what they can come up with on their own.

Create a Giving Calendar. This can be especially fun during the month of December, when there are many holidays that celebrate traditions with giving. Print off a blank calendar or use the one in this book. Plan one week at a time. Write down one name or category in each box. Give that person a gift on that day.

Giving Calendar

Write the name of one person or pet in each box. Then, think about what gift you can give. When that day comes, give the person or pet their present! Remember just your words or time count too, as long as it comes from your heart.

Monday	Tuesday	Wednesday	Thursday	Friday	Saturday	Sunday

Listen to this life advice.

When you give, it's super nice!

Plan a gift to give each day,

a friendly act or words to say.

It doesn't have to cost a dime,

a special gift can be your time!

Love to others, fills your heart!

Let's make a list of ways to start.

To Teachers

Draw a picture, make a card,
bring in flowers from the yard.
Organize and clean with friends,
thank them when the school day ends.

To Grandparents

Write a letter, share what's new.

Call and tell them, 'I love you!'

Laugh at all the jokes they tell.

Bring a flower, stone or shell.

To Pets

Time outside, a doggie toy,

throwing balls can bring them joy.

Pet them, snuggle, take a walk,

sing a song or speak sweet talk.

To Friends

Give a gift, a piece of art.

Paint a rock with stars or hearts.

Ride fast scooters, take a walk,

laugh and listen when they talk!

To Neighbors

Bring them treats you made to share.
A plate of cookies shows you care!
Weed their garden, shovel snow,
bring their mail in when they go.

 **To Sisters**

Ask to brush or comb her hair.

Lend your favorite toy to share.

Climb a tree or play pretend.

Tell her she's your
greatest friend!

To Aunts and Uncles

When they visit, give a squeeze.

Sit outside under trees.

Build a fort and read or hide,

snuggle closely by their side.

To People in Need

Donate clothes, a toy, a book,

help make lunches - you can cook!

Collect some food for folks near you,

like applesauce or cans of stew.

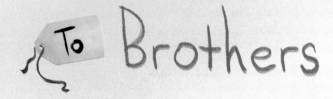

To Brothers

Race your bike or kick a ball,

help him up when he may fall.

No matter what

Challenges life brings,

remind him he

Can do great things.

To Parents

Do your chores right when you're told.

Be kind to siblings, young and old.

Tell them, 'thank you' out of the blue.

Explain you're **grateful** for all they do.

To Yourself

Lots of water, healthy foods,

they're good for you and help your moods.

Exercise and go outside,

ride a bike or use *a slide!*

Kind things you do can add right up.

Show some love to fill another's cup!

When you give, you receive too.

The magic of giving starts in you!

SPECIAL

AS CAN BE

THIS IS THE MAGIC OF ME!

YOUR PICTURE HERE!

Dear Readers,

Thank you for reading *My Magical Gifts* to your child or children. It's important to teach kids at a young age that they have so much to give! When kids see their words and actions as presents, they will feel empowered to help others. The more we give generously, the more we open ourselves to receive!

If you feel *My Magical Gifts* should be shared with others, the best way to help it reach more children is to leave an honest review on Amazon and share it on social media. Your words and photos will help others learn about my book and make it possible for me to keep on writing!

If you enjoyed this book, be sure to check out my other books in this series, *My Magical Words*, *My Magical Choices*, and *My Magical Dreams*.

Do you have an older child, age 8 or up? Then grab a copy of *The Magic of Me: A Kids' Spiritual Guide for Health and Happiness*. It contains 30 life-lessons every kid must learn for success in the real world.

Your support is a blessing. Thank you!

With love,

Becky

#themagicofme
@authorbcummings

Becky Cummings is an author, teacher and mom of three. She loves kids and speaking her truth. Becky is blessed to combine these passions by writing children's books that spread messages of love, hope, faith, health, and happiness. When she isn't writing, you might find her salsa dancing, eating a veggie burrito at her favorite Mexican joint, or traveling to new places! Becky is available for author visits and wants to connect with you so be sure to visit her on Facebook fb.me/authorbcummings, or Instagram and visit her website, www.authorbcummings.com.

Zuzana Svobodová is an illustrator. She uses both digital and traditional techniques, as well as the world of fantasy delivered happily by her two children to bring stories to life. When she isn't working on illustrations, she enjoys drawing, doing and teaching yoga, dreaming and baking sweets.